Watch Us Grow

 HOUGHTON MIFFLIN HARCOURT
School Publishers

Contents

TEKS **1.3A** decode words in isolation; **1.3C(vi)** decode using r-controlled vowel pattern; **1.3D** decode words with common spelling patterns

Phonics

Words with <u>ar</u> Read each word. Then use two words in a sentence.

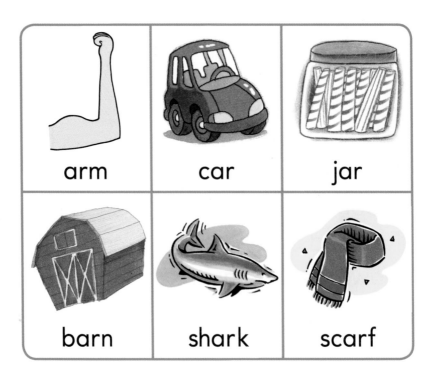

| arm | car | jar |
| barn | shark | scarf |

Mark Shark

by Melissa Rothman
illustrated by Teri Sloat

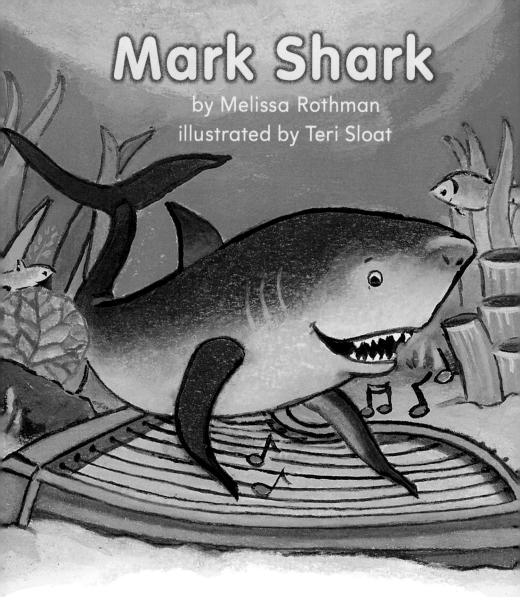

Mark Shark saw this harp in the
deep dark sea. Mark Shark had
never seen a harp. Can he play it?

Mark plucked at the strings, and sweet notes came out.

He played and played. Sweet tunes filled the sea.

Mark's pals had not seen him in a long time.

"I will swim and find Mark," said Carl. Will Carl find him?

Carl can hear sweet tunes. He
swam to see what made the sweet
tunes. Then Carl saw Mark and his
harp. Can Mark play it?

I didn't know you can play the harp," Carl told Mark.

"I just started and got better each day," said Mark.

Carl just had to tell his pals.
Carl and his pals swam back. His
pals sang to the sweet tunes that
Mark played.

Mark was a huge star.

Mark's pals asked Mark to teach them to play.

"It's not hard," said Mark.

Mark and his pals play,
and the dark sea is filled with
sweet tunes.

TEKS 1.9A retell story events; **ELPS** 4G demonstrate comprehension through shared reading/ retelling/responding/note-taking

Retelling

Read Together

Order of Events Read these events from "Mark Shark." The events are all mixed up.

- Mark played and played. His pals did not see him for a long time.
- Mark was a huge star.
- Mark saw a harp in the sea.

Work with a partner. Put the events in the correct order.

TEKS **1.3A** decode words in context and in isolation; **1.3C(vi)** decode using r-controlled vowel pattern; **1.3D** decode words with common spelling patterns

Phonics

Words with <u>ar</u> Read the story. Tell which picture goes with the end of the story. Then point to and read the <u>ar</u> words.

Mark got in the car and went to the park. His dog Spark went with him. When it got dark, they went back home.

Clark's Part

by Jay Griffin

illustrated by Adjoa Burrowes

"I got a part in the class show,"
Clark told Mom. "I will be a big dog
in the show."

"Five kids will put on dog masks
and capes. We will march on stage
and bark. Then we will say our
parts," said Clark.

"Let's start to read your part,"
said Mom. "Let's start."

14

While Clark rode his bike that weekend, he said his part. A cat darted in his way. Clark turned his bike. Clark missed that cat, but he fell hard on the park path.

Clark had sharp pain in his arm.
He needed a cast on his arm.

Clark had to start to do things
with his left hand.

His classmates wrote on his cast.

"Can you write?" asked Rick.

"Maybe with my left hand," said Clark.

"I hope you can still play your part," said Nell.

Mom is at the class show. Clark had on his mask and cape.

"Will you know me when I am on stage?" asked Clark.

"I will know your bark," said Mom, with a smile.

That night, five kids marched on
stage. Clark was not hard to see!

TEKS 1.1A recognize that print represents speech; RC-1(E) retell/act out important story events;
ELPS 1E internalize new basic/academic language

Words in Print

Read Together

Dialogue Read this play with a partner.

> **Clark:** "I broke my arm."
>
> **Rick:** "Can I write my name on your cast?"
>
> **Clark:** "Yes. Do you think I can still play my part?"
>
> **Rick:** "You can if you can still bark like a dog!"

Act It Out Now, act out what Clark and Rick say.

21

TEKS 1.3A decode words in isolation; **1.3C(vi)** decode using r-controlled vowel pattern; **1.3D** decode words with common spelling patterns

Phonics

Words with <u>ar</u>, <u>or</u>, and <u>ore</u>
Read the words on each shelf.
Then start over and point to and
read only words with <u>ar</u>. Repeat
with words with <u>or</u> and <u>ore</u>.

WORD STORE

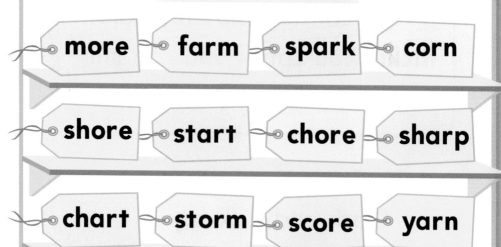

more   farm   spark   corn

shore   start   chore   sharp

chart   storm   score   yarn

More Fun for Jake

by Melissa Rothman

illustrated by John Hovell

Every day Jake's dad runs on
the shore. Dad runs and runs.

"When I grow up, I will run like my dad. I will be fast, and I will run far," thought Jake. "I will be fast like him."

One day Jake and his dad went
to a sports store.

"I like these green shorts and this
red cap," Jake told his dad.

When the weekend came, Dad asked Jake to run with him. Jake wore his green shorts and red cap. Dad and Jake ran and ran.

Each weekend Jake and Dad ran.
One day, Jake showed Dad a note.
It said, "Race for Dads and Cubs."
Can Dad and Jake race?

"Would you like to be in that
race?" Dad asked Jake.

"Yes, yes, yes!" said Jake. "I can
be in it."

On the day of the race, Jake
wore his green shorts and his red
cap. Mom came to clap for Jake
and Dad.

The race was more fun than Jake
thought it would be.

"Let's race!" yelled Jake.

"Yes we will, but let's wait for the
weekend," said Dad.

TEKS 1.1F Identify information provided by book parts; **1.19C** write brief comments on texts; **ELPS** 5G narrate/describe/explain in writing

Book Information

Read Together

Authors An **author** is a person who writes stories. Who wrote "More Fun for Jake?"

title →
author —
illustrator —

More Fun for Jake
by Melissa Rothman
illustrated by John Hovell

Write a Note Write a note to the author telling what you like or do not like about the story. Be sure to explain why.

Phonics

Words with <u>er</u>, <u>ir</u>, and <u>ur</u>
Read each word to go up and down the wall. Tell what middle sound all the words have. Name the different letters that spell that sound.

twirl

clerk turn

hurt third

girl germ

fern burst

See the Birds

by Susie Dietz

Look at this bird perched on a
tree branch. She has a sweet song.
Chirp, chirp, chirp. She can chirp a
pretty song.

It is fall. The bird that is perched in this tree will find lots to eat. Every time he turns, he will see a treat.

When it turns cold, it is hard to get food. This bird gets food in wet snow.

It is spring. This bird has made her nest with sticks, wet dirt, and soft grass. She sits in her nest.

Her eggs will be safe in this nest.
The chicks are curled up inside the
eggs. They will not be hurt.

The first baby bird will burst its
shell. The chick cannot see yet, but it
can peep.

Four baby birds sit in this nest.
They perk up when mom bird brings
food.

This is not a chick. It is a young
bird with dark spots. When she is
grown up, she will look just like her
mom. She will make her own nest
and have her own baby birds.

TEKS 1.14C retell order of events; **ELPS** 4G demonstrate comprehension through shared reading/ retelling/responding/note-taking

Retelling

Read Together

Order of Events Reread "See the Birds." Look at the pictures. What events happen in each season? Use the pictures to retell the events in order to a partner.

Then fill in a chart like this with things that happen each season.

Fall	Winter	Spring

TEKS **1.3A** decode words in context and in isolation; **1.3C(vi)** decode using r-controlled vowel pattern; **1.3D** decode words with common spelling patterns

Phonics

Words with <u>er</u>, <u>ir</u>, <u>ur</u> Read each sentence. Then look at the sentences again. Point to and read words with <u>er</u>, <u>ir</u>, or <u>ur</u>.

1. Her skirt twirls when she turns.

2. We planted a fir tree in the dirt.

3. The first bird is chirping.

A Bath for Mert

by Maryann Cristensen
illustrated by Lizi Boyd

"Where is Mert?" asked Kate.
Mert was curled up under the porch.
"She is sleeping in the soft dirt,"
said Burt.

Mert woke up and jumped to
greet Kate.

Kate turned and said, "Mert has
dirt on her fur. Mert needs a bath."

"Yes," said Burt. "Just follow me.
First, we fill this tub with water.
Then we stir in soap flakes."

Kate and Burt plunked Mert in
the tub. Kate and Burt had to scrub
hard until Mert was clean.

"Hold Mert for me," said Kate.
"Get a firm grip on her, so I can
squirt and take off the suds."

Kate grasped the hose to spray
Mert, but Kate sprayed Burt.

"Stop!" yelled Burt. "You're
squirting me. My shirt is soaked."

Then Mert started to shake,
shake, and shake.

"Stop, Mert," yelled Kate. "Don't
shake so much. My shirt and skirt
are soaked!"

"Mom, we gave Mert the best
bath," Burt boasted.

Mert barked and barked.

"Maybe Mert gave you baths,
too!" said Mom.

Use Strategies

Read Together

Read for Understanding Reread **A Bath for Mert** on pages 43–50 carefully.

Correct and Adjust As you read the story, you might not understand a part of it. Do one or more of these things to help you:

- Reread it aloud.
- Picture in your mind what it is about.
- Think about what you already know, such as the steps for taking a bath.
- Ask yourself a question about the meaning, such as **Why does Kate need to squirt Mert with water?**

TEKS 1.3A decode words in context and in isolation; **1.3C(vi)** decode using r-controlled vowel pattern; **1.3D** decode words with common spelling patterns

Phonics

Words with <u>er</u>, <u>ir</u>, and <u>ur</u> Read the story. Then point to and reread words with <u>er</u>, <u>ir</u>, and <u>ur</u>.

"It's my turn," said the girl in the yellow shirt. She hit the ball over the fir tree and into the ferns! The girl ran to first base and kept going. Her teammate ran to third base.

Meet Gert

by Carmen Santos
illustrated by John Kurtz

This is my friend Gert. She is eight years old. She is in third grade. I wrote about Gert. Turn the pages and meet Gert.

This is Gert at the beach with
her mom. She begins her day in the
shade. She doesn't want to burn.
She is reading about surfing.

This is Gert with her pictures of birds chirping. Gert likes to take pictures of birds perched in trees. Gert likes red birds. She likes red the best.

This is Gert on a team. She plays
sports with girls her age. Gert is good
at kicking. She and her teammates
have on red shirts and shorts.

This is Gert on skates. She has
on a green shirt and skirt. Gert
is just learning to turn on one leg.
Gert likes when her skirt spins.

This is Gert at a race. She has
on a white shirt and shorts. Gert is
crossing the red line first. She will
win first prize.

This is Gert in a pink skirt.
She has burst on to the stage and
is whirling and whirling. Gert has
fun whirling.

This is Gert with me. We met in
first grade. Now it is Gert's turn to
write about me!

TEKS **1.17E** publish/share writing; **1.19A** write brief compositions; **1.21B(iii)** capitalize names of people

Writing

Plan and Write Think about a good friend of yours. What does your friend like to do?

Write about your friend. Use adjectives to tell more. Share your work with a partner.

Remember Use a capital letter for your friend's name.

Phonics

Words with <u>oo</u> Read each word by itself. Point to <u>oo</u> in each word and say the sound it stands for. Read the words again.

hood

foot

cook

book

wood

hook

Look at This!

by Louise Tidd

illustrated by Marilyn Janovitz

"Mom," said Tad, "let's go for a
nice bike ride along the path."

Tad and Mom got on this big bike.
They took a ride on a bike path.

When Mom and Tad got back
again, Tad saw Trish.

"Let's go and see Trish," said Tad.
"Trish is in her yard."

"What is this?" asked Mom.

"I am planting seeds. Green
bean plants and green pea plants will
grow," said Trish. Then Trish stood up.

"Can we plant seeds, Mom?"
asked Tad. "It looks like fun."

"We can, but it is not just fun,"
said Mom. "It is work."

Trish gave them some seeds.

"Growing these plants is fun and work. If you work hard you will get a good prize," said Trish.

Tad and Mom took the seeds
and went home. Tad made holes in
the dirt. Then he put seeds in them.
Mom put dirt over the seeds that
Tad planted.

Tad and Mom had to water their plants and pull up weeds. Tad and Mom saw their plants grow big.

"Look," yelled Tad. "Look at these big plants."

"Look at these plants! What can
we do with them?" asked Tad.

"We can eat them," said Mom.

"Such good prizes!" said Tad.

TEKS **1.3H** identify/read high-frequency words; **1.5** read aloud with fluency/comprehension; **ELPS** **4G** demonstrate comprehension through shared reading/retelling/responding/note-taking

Fluency Read Together

Words to Know Write these words on cards.

> again   along   water   work

Work with a partner. Hold up a word card. See how quickly your partner can read it. Then switch roles.

Read Aloud Take turns reading "Look at This!" Read each word carefully.

TEKS **1.3A** decode words in context and in isolation; **1.3D** decode words with common spelling patterns; **1.3F** identify/read compound words; **1.3G** identify/read contractions

Phonics

Words with <u>oo</u> Read each sentence. Tell which picture goes with it. Then reread the words with <u>oo</u>.

1. I'm looking in a cookbook.

2. We stood in a long line.

3. You're a good dog!

Two Good Cooks

by Gretchen Nguyen

illustrated by Laura Rader

Mom is on her way home. Mom will be late. My father and I will cook. We began with a good plan.

We look at this shelf. We see
eggs and ham and cheese and milk.
Those will be good to cook with.

We take out eggs, ham, cheese
and milk. Then we get bowls and
forks and pans. We can't cook yet.

Dad hands me Mom's cookbook. It will tell us how to cook. We look at the page that shows us how to cook eggs. This is it!

This cookbook tells us to get eggs, milk, ham, and cheese.

"This looks good!" I say. "We have eggs, milk, ham, and cheese."

I mix eggs and milk. Dad cuts
ham and cheese into bits. Then I mix
ham and cheese in with the eggs.
Dad will heat the eggs, ham, and
cheese in a pan.

Just then I see Mom.

"That smells so good! What is it?" she asks. "Can I look?"

"Just sit and we will bring it to you," I say. "Then you can look."

Mom laughs and sits.

"This is a real treat. You and
Dad did a good deed!" said Mom.

TEKS 1.27A listen attentively/ask relevant questions; ELPS 2I demonstrate listening comprehension of spoken English; 3G express opinions/ideas/feelings

Connections

Read Together

Listening and Speaking Tell about a meal you would like to cook. What would you make? How would it smell? How would it taste?

With a partner, take turns sharing your ideas. Ask each other questions. Listen carefully when your partner speaks.

TEKS **1.3A** decode words in context and in isolation; **1.3C(i)** decode using closed syllables

Phonics

Words with Two Syllables

Read each sentence. Tell which picture it matches. Then reread the words with two syllables.

1. The kitten and the rabbit run.

2. Dennis has a yellow pencil.

3. Kristen stood on ladder to get the basket.

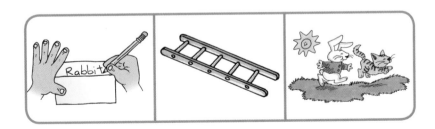

82

Big Problems

by Jackson Prescott
illustrated by Shari Halpern

Ray is a boy. He has a dog.
Ray's dog is Dennis. Dennis had
problems that began when he was
just a pup.

Dennis was much too big to fit in
his dog bed. It was a problem.
"Dennis needs a big bed," said
Ray. "Yes, Dennis needs a big bed."

Ray gave Dennis big soft yellow
pillows. Did Dennis like his yellow
bed? Dennis did. It was nice and
soft. Better yet, it was big.

As Dennis got big, his problems
got big as well. It was hard for Ray
to take Dennis for a walk.

"This is a problem," said Ray. "It
is a big problem."

So, Ray began to ride on, not
walk with, Dennis. Did Dennis like
this? Dennis did. Did Ray like this?
Ray did like it. Dad did, too.

"No problem," said Ray.

As Dennis got big, so did his problems. When Dennis stood up, he did not fit in his dog house.

"You need a big house," said Ray.

"We can make a big house for
Dennis," said Dad.

So Ray, his sister, and his dad
made a big house for Dennis.

Dennis and Ray can fit in the big
house. Dennis likes that. Ray likes
it, too. Dennis and Ray like to be
together.

"No problems," said Ray.

Retelling

Plot In the story "Big Problems," Ray and Dennis have problems. They come up with a solution to each problem.

Work with a partner. Decide what the problems are.
Then tell how they solve the problems.

Phonics

Words with <u>oo</u>, <u>ou</u>, <u>ew</u>

Read each word by itself. Does it have the same vowel sound as <u>moon</u>? Tell how the vowel sound is spelled in each word. Read the words again.

drew	broom
flew	new
you	knew
scoop	zoo

Moose's Tooth

by Paul Giuliano
illustrated by Sachiko Yoshikawa

Moose has a loose tooth. His
loose tooth feels funny. A loose
tooth can go back and forth.

Moose likes to eat water plants.
Moose has to get in deep water up
to his knees.

Moose dips down and scoops up
a plant. Moose's food is wet. Dip
and scoop! Dip and scoop!

Moose has a loose tooth. Now, Moose can't chew his food. Chewing can make his tooth too loose. Moose must get a new plan.

Moose has a new plan. Moose
takes his food inside. He knows just
what to do. If Moose can't chew, he
will mix a brew. That is his plan.

Moose adds plants and a flower
or two to the mix. His plant and
flower mix looks like thick green goop.

Moose adds milk. His green goop
shake is ready. Moose can drink it.
Moose has no need to chew!

Moose likes his new brew.
Moose's loose tooth likes it, too.

Vocabulary Read Together

Action Words Read the verbs.

> eat dip chew mix add scoop

Act It Out Work with a partner. Write each word on a card. Place the cards face-down. Pick a card and act out the word. See if your partner can guess it. Then have your partner act out a word and you guess the action.

TEKS **1.3A** decode words in context and in isolation; **1.3C(vi)** decode using r-controlled vowel pattern; **1.3F** identify/read compound words; **1.3G** identify/read contractions

Phonics

Words with <u>oo</u>, <u>ou</u>, <u>ew</u> Read the story. Find words with the same vowel sound as <u>moon</u>. Reread the words. Tell what letters stand for the sound.

Lou has a new plant in her bedroom. She waters it so it won't droop. She doesn't let her dog Scoot chew on it. Soon, Lou's new plant will bloom.

Moon News

by James Franklin

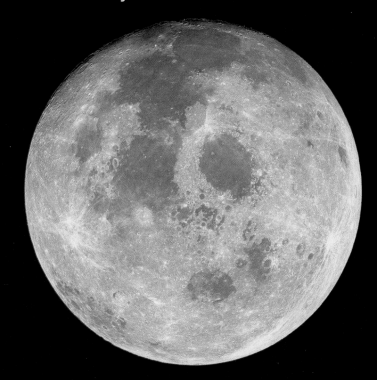

This is our moon. We can see the
moon at night. We cannot see the
moon at noon. That's a scoop! No
noon moon.

This is a full moon. It can look
white. It can look yellow. It can look
sort of red. A full moon is pretty,
white, yellow, or red.

This is a new moon. It looks like
a slice of moon. But it is not a moon
slice. A new moon shows just the
part that is lit up.

This moon chart shows you how the moon can look. This moon chart starts with the new moon on day 1. It shows the full moon on day 14.

Look at this painting. It shows
the moon and stars. Did the person
who painted this like the moon? Did
he add anything to it?

This painting shows the moon.
This painting also shows what the
moon shone on. It shone on land.
It shone on trees. Trees gleam in
the moon's glow.

This painting also shows the
moon. This painting shows what the
moon shone on. It shone on water.
Water gleams in the moon's glow.

Moon Song

I like to look at the moon,

and hope to visit it soon.

You can come, too.

You can be in my crew.

TEKS 1.8 respond to/use rhythm/rhyme/alliteration; 1.18B write short poems; ELPS 5B write using new basic/content-based vocabulary

Poems

Read Together

Plan and Write Think about how the moon looks. How does the moon make you feel? Write a short poem about the moon.

Remember

- Look for good words to use in "Moon News."
- Try to use some rhyming words.

Phonics

Words like <u>moon</u>

Read the rhyme. Reread words with the same vowel sound as <u>moon</u>.

It was a cool night in June.
A blue bird flew to the moon.
The bird crooned a sweet tune.
Then it flew home soon.
Do you think that bird knew
that its tune made the huge
moon blue?
Do you think this tale is true?

Red Zed and Blue Stu

by Kate Pistone

illustrated by Paulette Bogan

Red Zed is a mule. Blue Stu is a mule. Red Zed and Blue Stu live on the same hill. The hill has grass for them to eat.

One day, cool winds blew.

"Blue Stu, it is too cool on this
hill," said Red Zed.

Blue Stu did not say a thing. He
just ate grass.

"Let's look for a new home. I like warm places," Red Zed went on.

"Let me chew this last bit of grass. I will be ready at noon," said Blue Stu. "I need a few more chews."

Blue Stu and Red Zed left the hill.

They got in this crude boat.

Blue Stu rowed and rowed.

"Land ho!" yelled Red Zed. "Land ho! Land ho!"

"I hope there is grass," grunted Blue Stu.

"It is warm on this dune," said
Red Zed.

"Yes, but I need food," said Blue
Stu. "Let's look for grass."

"Yes, yes," said Red Zed. "Let's!"

Red Zed saw no grass.

"I need food, too," said Red Zed.
"I need food to eat."

"Let's go back to our cool hill,"
said Blue Stu. He had a plan.

Now, Red Zed and Blue Stu were
warm and full. They did not say a
thing. They just ate grass.

Use Strategies Read Together

Read for Understanding Reread **Red Zed and Blue Stu** on pages 113–120 carefully.

Correct and Adjust As you read the story, you might not understand a part of it. Do one or more of these things to help you:

- Reread it aloud.
- Picture in your mind what it is about.
- Think about what you already know, such as what animals need to live.
- Ask yourself a question about the meaning, such as **Why don't the mules like the dune?**

Phonics

Words with <u>ou</u> and <u>ow</u> Read the words in the clouds. Listen for the vowel sound. Reread the words, say the vowel sound, and then tell what letters stand for the sound.

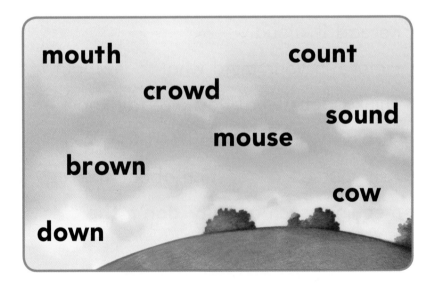

mouth count

crowd

sound

mouse

brown

cow

down

Down on the Farm

by Siri Hansen

It is spring on this farm. Come and see a farm animal here.

Up on a hill is a brown horse with white feet. Her foal is with her. Her foal is growing up now.

Out in the grass is a brown and white cow with her brown and white baby. Her baby is growing up now.

This cute wood mouse skips along
the ground. This mouse likes to sneak
into the barn. It likes to get bits of
food in the barn.

A barn owl sits in this barn. If
the mouse sees the barn owl, the
mouse will not go in. Barn owls help
keep mice out of barns.

Look at this proud mother pig and
her family. She sniffs the ground with
her snout. Soon her seven piglets will
be as big as their mom.

The wool coat on this mother
sheep is thick and soft! She is with
her lamb. Soon her lamb will have a
thick, soft coat, too.

This hen is with her baby chicks.
Her family stays with her for now.

It's spring down on the farm. It
is time to shout, "Come and see each
animal and its family!"

TEKS **1.10** distinguish true stories from fantasies; **1.19C** write brief comments on texts; **ELPS 4K** employ analytical skills to demonstrate comprehension

Kinds of Books

Read Together

Nonfiction or Fantasy If a story gives information about real animals, it is nonfiction. If the animals in a story do things that no real animals can do, the story is fantasy.

Write Work with a partner. Decide if "Down on the Farm" is nonfiction or fantasy. Write reasons why you think so.

TEKS **1.3A** decode words in context and in isolation; **1.3C(i)** decode using closed syllables; **1.3C(vi)** decode using r-controlled vowel pattern; **1.3E** read words with inflectional endings

Phonics

Words with <u>ou</u> and <u>ow</u> Read each clue. Tell which picture matches the clue. Point to and read words with <u>ou</u> and <u>ow</u>.

1. It comes from cows.

2. It comes down from a cloud.

3. It is worn by a clown.

4. Flowers in the ground need it.

Scout and Count

by Tawana Ross

illustrated by Philomena O'Neill

Scout sat on the couch when Dad came into the house. In his arms was a sweet brown and white pup.

"Miss Crown gave us this pup.
Will we keep him, Scout?"

"Wow!" said Scout. "Yes! Please,
let's keep him. He's so cute. He's a
sweet pup."

"What will we name him?" asked
Dad. "How about Sprout?"

Scout frowned. Then she asked,
"Can we name him Count?"

"Count is a good name," said Dad.

"Here, Count," Scout shouted as Count sniffed around his new house. Count did not come.

"I will teach Count myself," vowed Scout. "It will be like dog school!"

Scout found a bowl for food.
"Here, Count," shouted Scout.
Count did not come. So Scout
took that bowl to Count and fed him.
Count ate and ate

Scout found a brush for Count's coat. Scout did not see Count.

"Here, Count," shouted Scout.

Count did not come to her. So Scout found Count, sat down, and brushed his coat.

One day, Scout played out in the yard. Count sat with Dad. Count and Dad sat on the deck.

"Here, Count," shouted Scout. Count jumped down off the deck and ran to Scout.

"Wow! Count knows his name now!" shouted Scout.

"Bow wow," barked Count.

TEKS 1.6A identify nouns/verbs; 1.6D categorize words; ELPS 1C use strategic learning techniques to acquire vocabulary

Vocabulary

Verbs and Nouns Read these words:

> ate   couch   deck
>
> jumped   brushed

Use a chart like this to sort the words from the box that name actions and words that name things. Add more words.

Actions	Things

Phonics

Words with <u>oi</u>, <u>oy</u>, <u>au</u>, and <u>aw</u>
Read the words in each row.
Say the vowel sound you hear in
each word. Find the two rhyming
words in each row.

joy	saw	drawn	boy
haul	toys	hawk	noise
launch	choice	voice	lawn

Shawn's Toys

by Eileen Brady

illustrated by Steven Parton

Each day Shawn put coins in his
big plastic jar. Shawn would be glad
when his coins filled the jar. Soon
Shawn could buy a new toy.

At night, Shawn dreamed about toys. In his dreams, he saw rows and rows of toys. He had dream toys.

One day, Shawn put five coins in
his jar. "It's full," yelled Shawn.
No more coins would fit.

Shawn dumped his coins. Dad
joined Shawn as he counted his coins.

"Let's go to City Toys now. Do
you know just what you will get?"
asked Dad.

"No, but I will know it when I see
it," said Shawn.

Dad and Shawn entered City Toys.
Shawn saw rows of toys, just like in
his dreams.

Roy showed them toys. He
pointed to toy trains that could
haul loads.

Shawn saw trains, trains, trains.

Then Roy pointed at a toy boat. "This boat can be launched in a pond," said Roy. "It's so much fun. You will like this toy."

Shawn saw a brown stuffed toy
with black paws. He pointed at it.

"Please," shouted Shawn. "This is
it! I will buy this toy."

"This toy is the best for me," said
Shawn. "It is the best!"

"Good choice," said Dad. "Good
choice, Shawn. We will get that."

TEKS 1.20A(i) understand/use verbs; **1.29** follow discussion rules; **ELPS 3E** share information in cooperative learning interactions

Connections

Read Together

Share Imagine that you will get a new toy. Write about it. Use sentences that begin like the ones below. Tell a partner about the toy. Use future verbs like the ones in your sentences.

I am going to _____.
My toy will _____.
I will _____.

Remember Follow your class's discussion rules. Stay on topic and listen to your partner.

TEKS **1.3A** decode words in isolation; **1.3C(i)** decode using closed syllables; **1.3C(v)** decode using vowel digraph/diphthong patterns;

Phonics

Decode Words in Isolation   Use what you know about sounds and letters to read each word by itself.

Words with <u>oo</u> like foot

book	cook	hook	look
foot	good	wood	stood

Words with <u>aw</u> and <u>au</u>

saw	law	paw	haul
launch	lawn	fault	straw

Words with <u>oi</u> and <u>oy</u>

oil	boil	foil	soil
spoil	boy	joy	toy

Decode Words in Isolation Use what you know about sounds and letters to read each word by itself.

Words with <u>oo</u> like foot

took	book	cook	hook
foot	brook	stood	shook

Words with <u>aw</u> and <u>au</u>

dawn	lawn	hawk	haul
cause	sauce	crawl	shawl

Words with <u>oi</u> and <u>oy</u>

coin	join	soil	toil
boy	joy	soy	Troy

Phonics

Decode Words in Isolation   Use what you know about sounds and letters to read each word by itself.

Words with <u>oo</u> like <u>foot</u>

cook
look
good
wood
shook
hook

Words with <u>aw</u>, <u>au</u>

paw
claw
lawn
fault
launch
sauce

Words with <u>oi</u>, <u>oy</u>

joy
boys
coins
noise
choice
voice

Words with ow like cow

down
plow
brown
clown
crowd
crown
town

Words with aw, au

haul
fawn
yawn
draw
fault
crawl
straw

Words with oi, oy

boys
toys
soil
foil
broil
spoil
moist

TEKS **1.3A(v)** decode words with vowel digraphs; **1.3B** apply letter-sound knowledge to create words; **1.3C(i)** decode using closed syllables; **1.3C(v)** decode using vowel digraph/diphthong patterns;

Phonics

Decode Words in Isolation   Use what you know about sounds and letters to read each word by itself.

Words with <u>oo</u> and <u>ew</u>

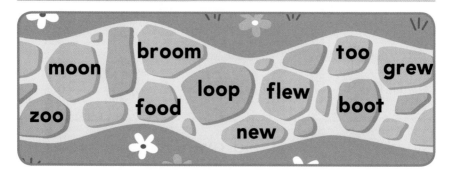

moon
broom
too
grew
loop
flew
food
boot
zoo
new

Words with <u>ow</u> and <u>ou</u>

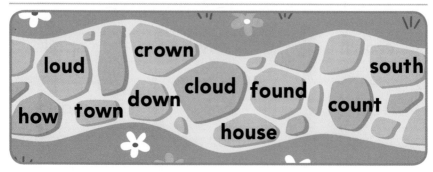

loud
crown
south
cloud
found
down
count
how
town
house

Build and Decode Words in Isolation   Put the letters together to read each word by itself. Think of more words to add.

ch ew	c ore
f ew	m ore
n ew	sh ore

c ow	p out
n ow	sh out
p l ow	s c out

p ool	j aw
c ool	p aw
s t ool	d r aw

157

Phonics

Words with <u>ew</u> Read each word by itself. Listen for the vowel sound. Point to the letters that stand for the sound. Read each word again.

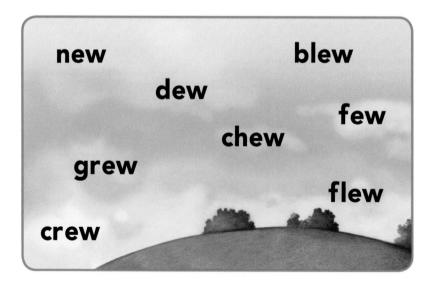

new

blew

dew

few

chew

grew

flew

crew

TEKS **1.3A(ii)** decode words with vowels; **1.3A(v)** decode words with vowel digraphs; **1.3C(i)** decode using closed syllables

Phonics

Words with <u>ou</u>, <u>ue</u>, <u>u</u>, and <u>ew</u>

Read each word by itself. Say the vowel sound you hear in each word. Tell what letters stand for the vowel sound. Read the words again.

few	blue	soup	chew
clue	flu	glue	threw
stew	you	true	grew

Word Lists

Accompanies *"The Tree"*

Mark Shark

page 2

Decodable Words
Target Skill: *r*-Controlled Vowel *ar*
Carl, dark, hard, harp, Mark, Mark's, Shark, star, started

Previously Taught Skills
and, at, back, came, can, day, deep, didn't, each, filled, got, had, he, him, his, huge, in, it, it's, just, know, long, made, not, notes, pals, play, played, plucked, sang, sea, see, seen, strings, sweet, swam, swim, teach, tell, that, them, then, this, time, tunes, will, with

High-Frequency Words
New
better, saw, told

Previously Taught
a, find, hear, I, never, out, said, the, to, was, what, you

Clark's Part

page 12

Decodable Words
Target Skill: *r*-Controlled Vowel *ar*
arm, bark, Clark, Clark's, darted, hard,
march, marched, park, part, parts,
sharp, start

Previously Taught Skills
am, and, asked, be, bark, big, bike,
but, can, cape, capes, cast, cat, class,
classmates, did, dog, fell, five, got, had,
hand, he, his, hope, in, kids, know, left,
let's, mask, masks, maybe, me, miss,
missed, Mom, needed, Nell, not, on,
pain, path, read, Rick, rode, say, see,
show, smile, still, stage, that, things,
then, way, we, weekend, when, while,
will, with, write, wrote

High-Frequency Words
New
night, told, turned

Previously Taught
a, do, I, my, our, put, said,
the, to, was, you, your

More Fun for Jake

Decodable Words

Target Skill: *r*-Controlled Vowels *or, ore*
for, more, shore, shorts, sports, store, wore

Target Skill: *r*-Controlled Vowel *ar*
far

Previously Taught Skills
and, asked, be, but, came, can, cap, clap, cubs, dad, dads, day, each, fast, fun, green, grow, him, his, in, it, Jake, Jake's, let's, like, Mom, note, on, race, ran, red, run, runs, showed, than, that, these, this, up, wait, weekend, went, when, will, with, yelled, yes

High-Frequency Words

New
thought, told

Previously Taught
every, I, my, of, one, said, the, to, was, would, you

See the Birds

page 32

Decodable Words

Target Skill: *r*-Controlled Vowels *er*, *ir*, *ur*

bird, birds, burst, chirp, curled, dirt, first, her, hurt, perched, park, turns

Previously Taught Skills

and, at, be, branch, brings, but, can, cannot, chick, chicks, dark, eat, eggs, get, gets, grass, grown, hard, has, he, in, inside, is, it, its, just, like, lots, made, make, mom, nest, not, own, this, time, on, peep, tree, safe, see, she, shell, sit, sits, snow, soft, song, spring, spots, sticks, sweet, that, treat, up, wet, when, with, will, yet

High-Frequency Words

New

baby, young

Previously Taught

a, cold, every, fall, find, food, four, have, look, pretty, the, they, to

163

A Bath for Mert

Decodable Words
Target Skill: *r*-Controlled Vowels *er*, *ir*, *ur*

Burt, curled, dirt, firm, first, fur, her, Mert, shirt, skirt, squirt, squirting, stir, turned

Previously Taught Skills
and, asked, barked, bath, baths, best, boasted, but, can, clean, fill, flakes, for, gave, get, grasped, greet, grip, had, hard, has, hose, in, is, jumped, just, Kate, maybe, me, Mom, much, needs, off, on, plunked, porch, scrub, shake, she, sleeping, so, soaked, soap, soft, spray, sprayed, started, stop, suds, take, this, then, tub, up, we, with, woke, yelled, yes

High-Frequency Words
New
follow, until

Previously Taught
a, are, don't, hold, I, my, said, the, to, too, under, was, water, where, you, you're

Meet Gert

page 52

Decodable Words
Target Skill: *r*-Controlled Vowels *er*, *ir*, *ur*

birds, burn, burst, chirping, first, Gert, girls, her, perched, shirts, skirt, surfing, third, turn, whirling

Previously Taught Skills
and, age, at, beach, best, crossing, day, fun, grade, green, has, in, is, it, just, kicking, leg, likes, line, me, meet, met, on, pages, pink, plays, prize, race, reading, red, shade, she, shorts, skates, spins, sports, stage, take, team, teammates, this, trees, when, white, will, win, with, write, wrote

High-Frequency Words
New
begins, eight, learning, years

Previously Taught
a, about, doesn't, friend, good, have, I, my, now, of, old, one, pictures, the, to, want

Look at This!

Decodable Words
Target Skill: Vowel Digraph *oo*
good, look, looks, stood, took

Previously Taught Skills
am, an, and, asked, at, back, bean, big,
bike, but, can, dirt, eat, for, fun, gave,
get, go, got, green, grow, growing, had,
he, her, holes, home, if, in, is, it, just,
let's, like, made, Mom, nice, on, path,
pea, plant, planted, planting, plants,
prize, prizes, ride, see, seeds, such,
Tad, that, them, then, these, this, Trish,
up, we, weeds, went, when, will, with,
yard, yelled

High-Frequency Words
New
again, along

Previously Taught
a, do, I, over, pull, put, said,
saw, some, the, their, they,
to, water, what, work, you

Two Good Cooks

page 72

Decodable Words

Target Skill: Vowel Digraph *oo*
cook, cooks, cookbook, good, look, looks

Previously Taught Skills

and, asks, at, be, bits, bowls, bring, can, can't, cheese, cuts, Dad, deed, did, eggs, forks, get, hands, ham, heat, her, home, in, is, it, just, late, me, milk, mix, Mom, Mom's, on, page, pan, pans, plan, real, say, see, she, shelf, shows, sit, sits, smells, so, take, tell, tells, that, then, this, those, treat, us, way, we, will, with, yet, you

High-Frequency Words

New

began, father

Previously Taught

a, have, how, I, into, two, laughs, my, out, said, the, to, two, you, what

Big Problems

page 82

Decodable Words

Target Skill: Syllable Pattern (CVC)
better, Dennis, pillows, problem,
problems, yellow, sister

Target Skill: Vowel Digraph *oo*
stood

Previously Taught Skills
and, as, be, bed, big, can, Dad, did,
dog, fit, for, gave, got, had, hard, has,
he, his, in, is, it, just, like, likes, made,
make, much, needs, nice, no, not, on,
pup, Ray, Ray's, ride, so, soft, take,
that, this, up, when, we, well, with,
yes, yet

High-Frequency Words
New
began, boy, house, together

Previously Taught
a, said, to, too, walk, was

Moose's Tooth

page 92

Decodable Words
Target Skill: Words with *oo, ou, ew*
brew, chew, chewing, food, goop, loose,
Moose, Moose's, new, scoops, too,
tooth

Previously Taught Skills
adds, and, back, can, can't, deep, dips,
drink, eat, feels, forth, get, go, green,
has, he, his, if, in, inside, is, it, just,
knees, knows, like, likes, looks, make,
milk, mix, must, need, no, or, plan,
plant, plants, shake, takes, that, thick,
up, wet, will

High-Frequency Words
New
flower, ready

Previously Taught
a, do, down, funny, now,
the, to, two, water, what

169

Accompanies
"A Butterfly Grows"

Moon News

Decodable Words
Target Skill: Words with *oo, ou, ew*
crew, moon, moon's, new, news, noon, scoop, soon, too, you

Previously Taught Skills
1, 14, add, and, at, be, but, can, cannot, chart, day, did, gleam, gleams, glow, he, hope, is, it, just, land, like, lit, look, looks, no, not, on, or, painting, painted, part, person, red, see, slice, shone, shows, song, sort, stars, starts, that, that's, this, trees, up, we, white, with, visit, yellow

High-Frequency Words
New
also, anything

Previously Taught
a, come, full, how, I, my, night, of, our, pretty, the, to, water, what, who

Red Zed and Blue Stu

page 112

Decodable Words

Target Skill: Words with *ue, u, u_e*
Blue, crude dune, mule, Stu

Target Skill: Words with *oo, ou, ew*
blew, chew, chews, cool, few, food, new, noon, too

Previously Taught Skills
and, at, ate, back, be, bit, boat, but, day, did, eat, for, got, grass, grunted, go, had, has, he, hill, ho, home, hope, in, is, it, just, land, last, left, let, let's, like, look, me, more, need, no, not, on, plan, Red, rowed, same, say, them, thing, this, will, winds, went, yelled, yes, Zed

High-Frequency Words

New
places, ready, warm

Previously Taught
a, full, I, live, of, one, or, said, saw, the, there, they, to, were

Down on the Farm

page 122

Decodable Words
Target Skill: Words with *ou, ow*
brown, cow, down, ground, mouse, now, out, owl, owls, proud, shout, snout

Previously Taught Skills
and, as, at, barn, barns, be, big, bits, chicks, coat, cute, each, farm, feet, foal, food, for, get, go, grass, growing, help, hen, her, hill, horse, if, in, is, it, its, it's, keep, lamb, likes, look, mice, mom, not, on, pig, piglets, see, sees, seven, she, sheep, skips, sits, sneak, sniffs, soft, soon, spring, stays, thick, this, time, too, up, white, will, with, wood, wool

High-Frequency Words
New
family, seven

Previously Taught
a, along, animal, baby, come, have, here, into, mother, of, the, their, to

Scout and Count

page 132

Decodable Words
Target Skill: Words with *ou, ow*
bow, brown, couch, Count, Count's, Crown, down, found, frowned, house, now, out, Scout, shouted, Sprout, vowed, wow

Previously Taught Skills
and, arms, as, asked, ate, barked, be, bowl, brush, brushed, came, can, coat, cute, Dad, day, deck, did, dog, fed, for, gave, good, her, he's, him, his, how, in, is, it, jumped, keep, knows, let's, like, Miss, name, new, nice, not, off, on, played, please, pup, ran, sat, see, she, sniffed, Sprout, so, sweet, teach, that, then, this, took, us, when, white, will, with, we, yard, yes

High-Frequency Words
New
myself, please, school

Previously Taught
a, about, around, come, here, I, into, the, one, said, to, was, what

Shawn's Toys

page 142

Decodable Words
Target Skill: Words with *oi, oy, au, aw*
choice, coins, haul, joined, launched, paws, pointed, Roy, saw, Shawn, toy, toys

Target Skill: Words with *ou, ow*
brown, counted, now, shouted

Previously Taught Skills
and, as, asked, at, be, best, black, big, boat, but, can, day, Dad, dream, dreamed, dreams, dumped, each, entered, filled, fit, five, for, fun, get, glad, go, good, had, he, his, in, is, it, it's, jar, just, know, let's, like, loads, me, more, much, new, no, plastic, please, pond, rows, see, showed, so, soon, stuffed, that, them, then, this, trains, we, when, will, with, yelled, you

High-Frequency Words
New
buy, city, please

Previously Taught
a, about, could, do, I, night, of, one, put, said, the, to, what, would